Maths with Ben

Enrichment Activities

F. R. (Joe) Watson

Association of Teachers of Mathematics

Published in April 2006 by The Association of Teachers of Mathematics

The Association of Teachers of Mathematics

Unit 7 Prime Industrial Park

Shaftesbury Street

Derby

DE23 8YB

Telephone: 01332 346599

Fax: 01332 204357

e-mail: admin@atm.org.uk

Maths with Ben

ISBN 1 898611 42 4

Maths with Ben

Introduction

These topics have been used at various times with able children in Years 5 and 6; they have also been used with Year 3. Several of the ideas can easily be extended into the secondary classroom or even used with younger children. The aim of the activities is to provoke thought and although some of the ideas might be encountered later, they are considered as material for enrichment rather than acceleration.

The origins of these activities

Some years ago a local school contacted the Keele Department of Education to enquire if was anyone available to give provide mathematics sessions for a year 6 pupil who was very able and not sufficiently challenged by the routine work. I agreed and worked with Ben over a two year period, seeing him about once a week/fortnight for about one and a half hours.

It was made clear at the outset, and the school accepted, that the work would be enrichment and not acceleration; the aim was to give Ben material which he would probably not encounter in the near future as this would make him even more 'out of step' with his classmates and make the mismatch even worse.

I was in the happy position of being able to use my own choice of topics with a pupil who was quick and keen to learn. When Ben left for a local Secondary school (where he is now in the Upper Sixth), I was asked to continue with two other boys from the new Year 7, and the activity has mushroomed. Currently I have four pupils from Year 5 and two groups of four, with one boy and three girls in each, for about three-quarters of an hour each once a week.

We work in a small music/study/store room next to the Headteacher's office, sitting around a table, the children on one side and I on the other. Initially I tended to set optional homework, saying, "Have a look at this for next time and tell me how you got on", but frequently Ben had done the problems but forgotten to bring the results, so we couldn't follow it up. Children occasionally want to try to solve a problem "for next time" and do so. Sometimes a topic has occupied the whole of a three-quarter hour session, but usually we look at two or three, often taking things up on a later occasion. We usually end with a game or puzzle – the '21 game' is popular as the group try to beat me, though it does get rather noisy … fortunately, the Head doesn't seem to mind.

I began to write up the material so that the class teacher would know what we had done – and would be in a position to use any of it should she wish. I did consider writing up some of the anecdotal material on Ben's responses, but never found time … !

I would like to thank the staff and pupils of the Hugo Meynell Primary School, Market Drayton, for giving me the opportunity of to work with Ben and his successors.

Maths with Ben Contents

Enrichment ideas

Strategy Games for two Players

Photocopiable Resources

Triangles into Hexagons

You need

Some equilateral triangles in two different colours.

Activity

Take four triangles of one colour and two of the other.

Arrange the triangles in a hexagon shape.

How many different patterns can you find?

This is one

How can you be sure you have found them all?

Now make a hexagon from three triangles of one colour and three of the other.

How many different patterns are there now?

Are you **sure** there are no more?

Explain your thinking.

What other numbers of the two colours could you use?

Teacher's Notes

The other two possible hexagons are

Once the first triangle is placed there are only three positions for the second one which give a different pattern.

When using three triangles of each colour, the following are possible

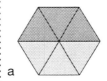 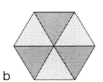

a   b

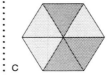

c   d

c and d are different because they are mirror images.

Encourage children to explain why there are no more.

Teacher's Notes

New shapes from Triangles

Six triangles can be arranged in different ways using the rule that edges match edges

and

are not allowed!

Here is one to start you off

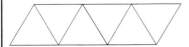

Investigate how many different arrangements of six triangles you can find.

Once you have found as many shapes as you can, choose one of the shapes, for example

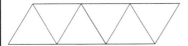

How many different ways can you make your shape using two triangles in one colour and four in another colour, e.g. two red and four yellow triangles?

What numbers of red and yellow triangles can you try next?

Teacher's Notes

It is possible to make twelve different shapes, or nineteen if reflections are counted.

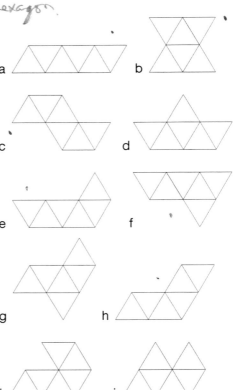

Using, for example, two red and four yellow triangles, there are nine different ways to colour shape (a)

The results with two red and four yellow for the other shapes are

Hexagon	3 ways
a, b, c, d, h and k	9 ways
e, f, g, I and l	15 ways

The results with three red and three yellow are

Hexagon	4 ways
a, b, c	10 ways
d, k	13 ways
e, f, g, i, j, l	20 ways

Coloured Corners

You need

Some equilateral triangle MATs.

Can you make them look different by putting a blob of coloured paint on one or more of the corners?

How many different triangles can you make?

Draw the triangles you have made and do not forget to include one without a blob of paint.

Now try doing the same problem using squares.

Try to guess first how many different squares you will be able to make.

Draw the squares you found.

Which regular shapes will you try next? Estimate first how many ways you can make the shape look different.

Mathematical Activity Tiles (MATs) are available from the Association of Teachers of Mathematics (ATM) www.atm.org.uk
The shapes available are equilateral and isosceles triangles, squares, rectangles, and also regular pentagons, hexagons, octagons.

Teacher's Notes

It is important to encourage children to investigate as far as hexagons to find out what happens to the pattern.

The solution using triangles

The solution using squares

The solution using regular pentagons

The solution using regular hexagons

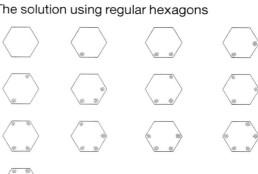

Using the number of solutions for triangles (4), squares (6) and pentagons (8) it is understandable if children estimate there will be 10 solutions for regular hexagons. In fact there are 13, or 14 if reflections are allowed.

All in Order

You need

Some different coloured counters (for example, red, blue, green, yellow, white).

Take three different coloured counters and arrange them in a row

How many **different** ways can you arrange the counters in a row?

Can you explain why the counters cannot be arranged in any more ways?

Extension

Now try the same problem using four counters, each in a different colour.

How many different ways can you arrange them in a row?

Investigate what happens if you have 5 counters … 6 counters … 7 counters …

Can you explain how you worked?

Factorials

We write 5 x 4 x 3 x 2 x 1 as 5! ("5 factorial").

Can you work out the value of 5! ?

How big is 10! ? Explain how you can work it out.

Now solve this problem

At midday, Annie and Ben are each given the number one.
After one hour, Annie multiplies her number by five and Ben multiplies his number by two.
At two o'clock, Annie again multiplies her number by five and Ben multiplies his number by three.
At three o'clock, Annie multiplies by five and Ben by four.
They continue with Annie multiplying by five every hour and Ben multiplying by one more than the previous time.

Does Ben ever catch up with Annie?
If so, at what time?

Teacher's Notes

There are six ways to arrange the three different coloured counters. One counter is chosen to put down first and then, the others can be placed in two ways. There are three choices for the first counter, which gives 3 x 2.

A variation for younger children is to give three different colours of car and to ask them to find different ways to park them if there are three spaces. Say that the important thing is the colour and parking place of the car and not the way it faces.

Parking Spaces

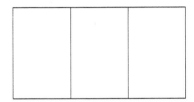

Extension

Children can explore the extension activity practically but with 24 possibilities it can become difficult for them to keep track of the work.

With four different colours of counter there are four choices for the first one, and the other three can be arranged in six ways as in the first part of the activity, so the answer is 4 x 6 = 4 x 3 x 2.

Assuming children understand why the result is 4 x 3 x 2 the investigation can be extended to using five counters and then, six counters etc.

Factorials

The answer to 10! is about 3.6 million. Give an interesting context for the investigation by linking it to a competition on a cornflakes packet in which the 10 attributes of a car must be put in the 'correct' order.

Now solve this problem

By 9 o'clock, Ben is ahead.

Triangular Arithmogons

Add pairs of numbers at each corner (vertex). Write the answers in the circles halfway along the line.

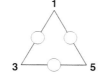

Use the numbers along the sides of the triangle to decide which numbers should be written at the corners.

Now try this one

Harder problems

Make up some more problems of your own and ask your partner to find the solutions. Explain what you did.

Talk to your partner about how the solutions were found.

Can you make up problems that do not use fractions?

How can you create problems that avoid negative numbers?

Teacher's Notes

Where children have to find the corner numbers their methods might include

a) Random guessing

b) Trying pairs of numbers that add to one of the numbers along the edge.

These are the approaches most likely to be used by younger children. It might be worth hinting at the following methods for solving the middle problem and others like it.

c) Try 1 at the top and work round clockwise. This gives 1, 4, 0, which does not work. Next try 2. This gives 2, 3, 1, the correct answer.

d) If we add the 3 and the 5 then we're counting both the left hand side of the triangle and the right hand side - this means that the top number has been counted twice - and the bottom two numbers have been counted just once. We know the bottom two numbers add up to four, so we can deduct this - and be left with just double the top number. So we know that the top number is 2 … and the rest is easy!

e) A sophisticated method is to use algebra. Let the numbers be x, y, z. Then, $x + y = 5, y + z = 4$, $z + x = 3$; therefore, $y = 3, z = 1$ and $x = 2$. In fact, this is a formal way of explaining method (d).

f) An easier algebraic explanation, which corresponds to method (c), is to let the top number be x, which makes the right hand number $5 - x$, and the left hand number $4 - (5 - x)$. So x plus $x - 1 = 3$ and so x must be 2.

Harder problems

The simplest way to solve this problem is to construct examples by working backwards from the answers. Suggest to children they think about odd and even numbers because if all three numbers are odd, or if just one is odd, all the corner numbers will involve halves. If all the numbers are even, or if just one is even, there will be no fractions.

There will be no negative number answers provided that the sum of any two of the circled numbers is greater than the third. This also means that the three lengths could be used to draw a triangle.

Square Arithmogons

Add pairs of numbers at the corners of the squares and write the answers in the circle on the side that joins the corners.

Now try to find the numbers that should be at the corners of the squares.
The pairs of numbers should add up to the numbers in the adjoining circle.

Here is another one to try

The next one is hard

Now try these numbers along the edges of your squares

a) 2, 6, 8, 4, e.g.

b) 5, 9, 7, 3

c) 3, 2, 6, 8

d) 5, 1, 1, 5

e) 5, 1, 5, 1

f) 1, 2, 3, 4

g) 1, 2, 4, 3

h) Make up your own square.

Now investigate pentagons in the same way.

Work with a friend to investigate hexagons, heptagons, octagons or …?

Write what you notice about them.

Teacher's Notes

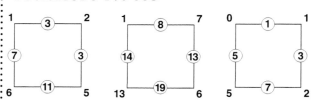

The answers to the two problems where corner numbers must be found are not unique.
Using algebra the four numbers of the first problem, where x is any number, are

$$x, 8 - x, 5 + x, 14 - x$$

For the second solution the numbers are

$$x, 1 - x, 2 + x, 5 - x$$

There is no solution to the harder problem. Method (c), that was used to solve the triangle arithmogons, is useful for finding solutions to the first three problems.

Of the sets of numbers (a) to (g) that children are given to find solutions, it is not possible to solve (c), (e), and (f). Children may notice that $6 + 4 = 2 + 8$ and, in general, that the sums of opposite sides are the same, for a solution to be possible.

Other shapes

Pentagons and heptagons behave like triangles because there is only one solution. Hexagons and octagons behave like squares in that there may not be a solution.

However, if there is a solution it is not unique and may be found using the methods given for solving square arithmogons.

The condition for a solution is that the two sums of sides taken alternately must be the same, e.g. 2, 3, 4, 5, 6 has four solutions, since $2 + 4 + 6 = 3 + 5 + 4$, but 2, 4, 3, 5, 6, 4 does not have solutions because $2 + 3 + 6 \neq 4 + 5 + 4$.

Hats problems

Three children are sitting in a circle. They are each wearing a paper hat. The three hats are coloured, e.g. one is red, one green and one yellow.

Each child can see two other hats but not their own hat. How will each child be able to tell their hat colour?

What if …?

Two children sit one behind the other, facing the same direction and both are wearing a hat. They know one hat is red and one is yellow.

The one at the back has to say if her hat colour is known but not what the colour is. Then the front person has to say if her hat colour is known.

Explain.

Next …

Two children sit one behind the other. Each of them is wearing a hat but this time their hats are chosen from red, red, yellow.

Can each child say if the colour of their hat is known this time? The back person says first if he knows his hat colour but does not say what it is.

Explain.

Is there only one way?

Talk to your friends about possible solutions.

A harder problem

Three children sit in a line, one behind the other. They are wearing hats chosen from red, red, red, yellow, yellow.

Starting with the one at the back, each child says if they know their hat colour.

Teacher's Notes

These logic problems come in varying degrees of difficulty. No mirrors are used in any of the problems; each person tells the truth and explains their reasoning logically.

The first problem was explained by Lauren, aged 5, "You look for the hat that is not there".

In the second problem only the person sitting behind can tell their hat colour because the other person's hat can be seen.

Next …

If the back person says he knows his hat colour he must be looking at a yellow hat and so, his hat is red. If he does not know the colour, he is looking at a red hat and so, his hat is either red or yellow. The one in front always knows his hat colour.

A harder problem

The person sitting at the back can always tell the colour of their hat.

Challenge

The Venusians are very intelligent people. They never tell lies and never guess answers to problems.

Twelve Venusians sit in a circle, each wearing a hat. They know there are two yellow hats and a large number of red ones. What they do not know is that they are all wearing red hats.

After 10 seconds ask who knows their hat colour. No one does know.

After another 10 seconds ask if anyone knows their hat colour … and after another 10 seconds. Finally everyone will know because they will realise that none of them can see two yellow hats.

This problem could be simplified by saying that there is one yellow and 12 red hats. In which case no-one will call after 10 seconds, so therefore …

A Square into Squares

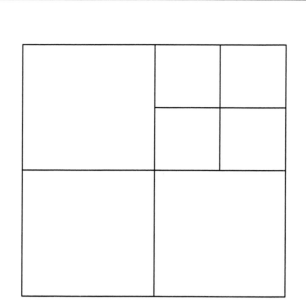

This square has been divided into seven smaller squares.

Can you find a way to divide a square into six squares? The squares do not all have to be the same size.

Find a way to divide the six squares into nine squares.

What other numbers of squares can you make?

To help you get started decide how you can change the pattern in the picture of seven squares.

Investigate ways to divide a large square into any number of smaller squares.

Teacher's Notes

Here are the solutions for six and nine squares.

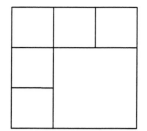 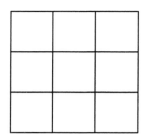

To help children find other numbers of squares suggest they start by finding more ways to divide the seven square and to record the number of squares each time.

It is possible to make all the numbers greater than five.

Questions to ask

• You have made seven squares. How can you change it to give more squares?

• How can you change a ten square pattern into one with thirteen squares?

• How can you change a six square into an eight square pattern?

• Can you put all your square patterns into order?

If N is possible, so is N + 2. Use this to show that 6, 8, 10, 12 etc are possible.

If N is possible, so is N + 3. Use this to show that 4, 7, 10, 13 etc are possible.

One stage in solving this problem is to notice that it is always possible to make the sum of 2 squares minus 1, e.g. 4 + (4 − 1) or 4 + (9 − 1) or 9 + (4 − 1) etc.

Golden Shapes

You need

A Golden Shapes resource sheet.

Imagine that all these shapes are made of gold.

Shape A is worth £1.

Work out the value of all the other shapes.
Explain what you did.

What was the value of triangles A, J and Q?
Which other triangles have the same value?

What other shapes have a value of £1?
What is the same and what is different about these shapes compared with the triangles?

Draw a shape with a value of £5.
Explain how you worked this out and then draw some different shapes with the same value.

Teacher's Notes

Children need a copy of the Golden Shapes resource sheet on page 32

This activity is about area, but this fact need not be mentioned. No mention is made of formulae such as length x breadth or length x breadth ÷ 2. So if Shape A has an area of one triangle and is worth £1 children will need to find shapes with the same or multiples of the same area as A to find the value. Try to let children work out values for themselves and explain what they did.

Once children are confident with ways of finding the value based on area, begin to ask questions …

- Find triangles with dots on the vertices but no dots inside or along the edges. What are they worth?

- What do you notice about shapes with one dot inside?

- What can you say about the shapes that are worth £2? Or £6?

Look at a number of shapes with *e* dots on the edges, *v* dots at the vertices and none inside, where *e* and *v* are kept constant with values like 2 and 3, and no greater than 5. Ask children if they can suggest a formula (or rule) which connects *e* and *v* with *A*, the area or 'value' of the shape.

Extend the questioning by asking children to look at shapes with one dot in the middle and ask how the formula changes. Continue by asking what happens if there are two, or three, dots in the middle. The aim is for children to explore the situation and **NOT** to teach them a formula.

Two-piece puzzles

You need

You need a copy of the two-piece puzzle resource.

Choose one of the shapes on the resource sheet and make two copies of it. Turn each one over and mark it with a coloured cross.

With your two shapes the same way up, put them together to make a new shape, using the rule that shapes must join along a whole side.
For example

This shape is allowed

But this shape is not allowed

Work with a friend to make as many different shapes as you can. Draw the shapes as you make them and write their names.

How can you be sure that you have made all the possible shapes?

Turn one of the pieces over. How many different two-piece shapes can you make now?

Teacher's Notes

If this activity is used with younger children suggest they draw round the new shapes and cut them out.

This will help to avoid duplication.

The names can be written on each shape.

Suggest children work in groups of four with each child using a different shape.

Based on an idea from Bob Vertes.

Two-piece puzzle resource on page 33

Three-piece puzzles

You need

You need a copy of the Three-Piece Puzzle Resource.

Cut along the dotted lines so you have three shapes. Draw a cross on the back of each shape with the same colour of pen.

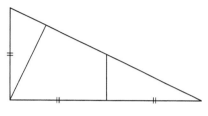

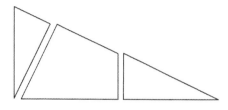

Place the shapes the same way up. You will make new shapes by putting shapes together along sides that are equal in length. For example

This shape is allowed

But this shape is not allowed

How many different shapes can you make using any two of the three pieces?

Draw the new shapes and write their names.

Explain how you know there are not any more shapes to make.

How many different shapes can you make using all three pieces? Draw the shapes and write their names.

Next Steps

Turn over one of the pieces and see how many different shapes you can make with these three pieces.

Next, turn over two pieces and explore the number of shapes.

What do you notice about the shapes you have made?

Teacher's Notes

Before starting this activity it might help to discuss the properties and names of familiar shapes, both regular and irregular.

Using the three pieces in the different ways it is possible to make at least 56 different shapes, 36 of which are convex. To help children find as many shapes as possible encourage them to work collaboratively and produce one piece of work between them. Suggest they look for both convex and concave shapes.

Convex

Concave

Also based on an idea from Bob Vertes.

Two-piece puzzle resource on page 33

Multiples of 3

Look at these numbers

9 7 247 102 39 45 73

Some of the numbers divide exactly by 3 and others do not.

Arrange the numbers into two columns – those which divide exactly by 3 and those that do not divide by 3.

Numbers that divide by 3	Numbers that do not divide by 3
9 102	7 247

Choose some numbers of your own and decide which column they go into.

Next add up the digits of each number you have tested until you only have a single digit.

For example the sum of the digits of the number 365 is 3 + 6 + 5 = 14, and if you add the digits of the answer 1 + 4 = 5.

The sum of the digits 12345 is
1 + 2 + 3 + 4 + 5 = 15
and 15 is 1 + 5 = 6.

What do you notice?

Try some very hard numbers.

Does the rule still work?

Find out if the same thing happens for 5 or for 7.

Weighty Problems

You have a beam balance.

If two objects are the same weight the pans will be level.

If one object is heavier than the other the balance will go down on that side.

Now try these problems

You have three coins. Two are genuine, but one is too light because it is counterfeit. Find the fake coin in one weighing.

Explain what you did.

You have nine coins. Eight of the coins are genuine, but one is too light. Find the fake coin in two weighings.

Explain how you solved the problem.

You have one coin that you know is genuine and you have four others. One of these you know is a fake but you do not know if it is too light or heavy. Find the fake coin in two weighings.

What did you do this time?

You have four objects that all look alike, but they have different weights. Arrange them, in order, from lightest to heaviest using five weighings at most.

Explain.

Teacher's Notes

The first two solutions are easy, the third is harder and the fourth may need demonstrating, although children need to try and think of possible solutions first.

For the first solution two coins are balanced. If they balance the third one must be the counterfeit; if they do not balance the lighter coin is counterfeit.

Choose six of the coins for the second problem. Weigh three against three. Continue as for the first solution, using the three lighter coins if they do not balance and the remaining three if they do balance.

To find the third solution choose any two of the four coins and balance them against each other. If they balance, both are good; if they do not balance, one of them is fake. In either case, we have two coins, one of which is known to be fake. Weigh one against the good coin; if they balance, the other is the fake, although we don't know in every case whether it is heavy or light.

An alternative method, which identifies the fake coin and also tells us whether it is **H**eavy or **L**ight is to let g be the good coin, a, b, c, d the others. Balance $a + g$ against $c + d$. If they balance, the fake is b and another weighing completes. If they do not balance, either a is heavy or one of c, d is light (or vice versa, according to the result). Now try c, d. If they balance, the fake is a which is heavy; if not, the one which is light is identified.

Use $a > b$ to mean 'a is heavier than b' to find the fourth solution. Use two weighings to find two pairs with $a > b$ and $c > d$. Then weigh a against c and suppose $a > c$. We now have $a > c > d$, and $a > b$, (after three weighings). Finally weigh b against c and, if necessary, b against d. This gives five weighings at most.

Sort the Symmetry

Discuss some of the things you know about symmetry with a friend.

You need the Symmetry resource sheet with these shapes

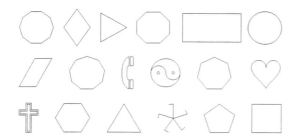

Draw all the lines of symmetry you can find for each shape.

Cut out the shapes and sort them with these headings

One line of reflective symmetry	More than one line of reflective symmetry	Rotational symmetry

Some shapes may go in more than one place.

These capital letters have been put into columns using a rule.

Can you say what the rule is and write headings to the columns?

A	B	H	J	S
T	C	X	F	N

Where will you write the letters D, G, I, K and Z?

Write in all the other letters of the alphabet.

Now put the digits 0 – 9 in their correct columns.

Teacher's Notes

This activity can be extended by suggesting children look for other shapes. Car logos and hubcaps provide especially interesting sources for investigation. Children can also look at naturally occurring examples of symmetry, such as insects, flowers etc.

Suggest children combine letters to write words that have vertical or horizontal symmetry.

They can also explore writing the top half of the words with horizontal symmetry and then, use a mirror to reveal the whole word. Alternatively, they could draw the top half of one word, and the bottom half of another word, but draw them together, e.g.

Symmetry resource sheet on page 35

Rotational Symmetry

Draw a shape with a horizontal mirror line

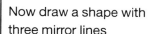

Draw a shape with two mirror lines

Now draw a shape with three mirror lines

This shape has a centre of rotational symmetry. The centre is shown by a dot. If you turn it through 1/3 of a complete turn, it looks the same.

Use dots to mark the centre of the three shapes you have drawn.

Take a piece of card shaped like a trapezium.

Draw a curved line to make two shapes, A and B.

Cut out shapes A and B.

Draw around shape B to make a symmetrical pattern like this.

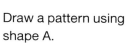

Draw a pattern using shape A.

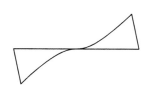

Next draw these patterns.

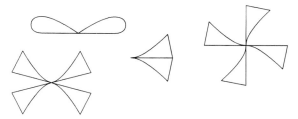

Make some patterns of your own using shape A or shape B, which have one or more lines of symmetry.

Teacher's Notes

These ideas can be explored in many computer programs. The drawing toolbar in Microsoft Word allows simple rotations and reflections. These shapes, based on a triangle, give one example.

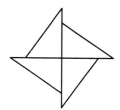 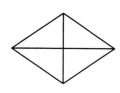

Another idea is to ask children to make a set of four identical square tiles that are divided into halves along the diagonal and each half is coloured differently.

They investigate different ways to arrange the four tiles into a 2 x 2 square and sketch each new arrangement. The new tiles are cut out and sorted into those with reflective, rotational or no lines of symmetry.

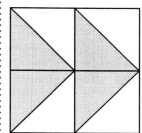 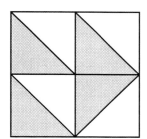

Wallpapers

You can make a simple repeating pattern by drawing a small motif or symbol at each corner of a grid.

The example uses a symbol like this ♩

Design a symbol of your own and repeat it at each corner of a grid.

Describe your pattern.

A different symbol and grid are used for this pattern

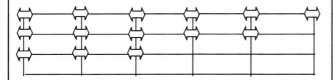

What do you notice about the symmetry in this pattern?

Design your own symbol to repeat on a grid.

Show any mirror lines and centres of rotation that you can find.

Teacher's Notes

Children can be encouraged to vary the way that the shape is repeated across the grid, for example by rotating it as well as moving to a new grid position.

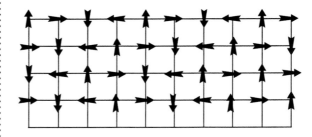

The design can also be reflected.

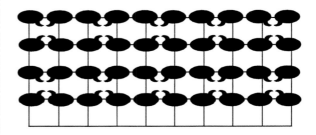

In each instance ask children to explain how the grid has been used.

Continue by using other grids, such as triangular or hexagonal grids.

There are 17 different sorts of wallpaper designs like this. It is worth exploring the Internet for other ideas.

www.atm.org.uk has some ideas

www.nrich.maths.org.uk has some more ideas

www.geom.uiuc.edu/java/Kali/ gives online interactive explanations.

Paper Symmetry

Fold a piece of paper once and cut a straight line at the fold line.

Fold another piece of paper twice and cut on the fold.

Fold three times and cut.

Name the shapes you have made.

Make more different shapes and write the names of the shapes on the folded paper. Try to make a square, a kite, a heart shape, a doily pattern, a string of people with their hands joined.

Can you make a parallelogram?

Fold an octagon.

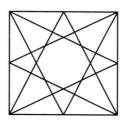

Can you see the octagon in the centre of this square of paper?

Work out how to fold and cut the paper so that you have an octagon.

Have you made a regular octagon? Explain your answer.

How many lines of symmetry can you find in your octagon?

Teacher's Notes

Although the sides of the octagon are equal it is not a regular shape. Children could investigate this by folding.

Paper Fractions and Folding Angles

Take a sheet of A4 paper.
How many different ways can you fold the paper in half so that the two halves fit on top of each other? Now find as many different ways as you can to fold the paper into quarters.

If you fold a sheet of paper in half, the thickness of the paper is doubled. Fold again and the thickness is multiplied by four.

If it was possible to fold the paper 30 times, how thick do you think the pile of paper would be?

What if the paper was folded 50 times?

A5 paper is half the size of A4, but it is the same shape?

Fold and cut (or tear carefully) sheets of A4, A5 and A6 paper. Arrange the paper as in this diagram.

Continue folding and then, halving the paper until you have about 10 pieces of paper of different sizes that meet at one corner. Can you work out what fraction each piece of paper is of the original size.

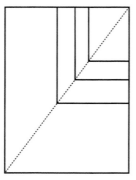

Fold a piece of paper to show an angle of 90°.

Can you fold an angle of 45°? Explain what you did.

Here is a way to fold an angle of 60° using A sized paper.

Fold the paper in half lengthwise and open it out.

Fold A to fall on the line LM at C to give the line BD.

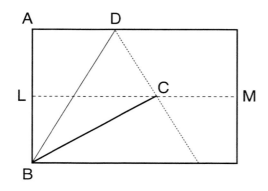

Teacher's Notes

When paper in the A series is folded and cut into half one gets a never-ending family of similar rectangles.

This is possible because the ratio of the sides, 1:√2, remains constant when the paper is halved.

The area of A0 paper is one square metre, A1 is half a square metre and therefore, A4 paper is one sixteenth of a square metre.

Square Numbers

You need

Counters or cubes in different colours

How many counters do you need to make the next size of square?

And the next one … ?

Draw a picture to show what you did.

The first square you made has 4 counters arranged in 2 rows of two. We write this as $4 = 2 \times 2 = 2^2$

The next square is written as $9 = 3 \times 3 = 3^2$.

Write the number sentences under your pictures.

Now complete the following

$36 = ? \times ?$

$? = 7 \times 7 =$

$? \times ? = 8^2$

These are called square numbers.

Can you explain why?

Write the first 10 square numbers starting with 1.

Find the square numbers on a 1–100 square. What do you notice?

Explain why the pattern looks as it does.

Find the differences between the square numbers.

Continue the pattern. Explain what you notice about this pattern.

Teacher's Notes

This is a good activity for introducing children to square numbers, especially if they make the patterns practically, either with counters or interlocking cubes. This will give a better understanding of how the square numbers have equal numbers in each row and column. To make each new square number one counter is added to each row and column, with an additional one at a corner.

Another interesting image to work with is this representation of square numbers:

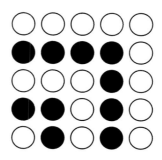

Square Number Problems

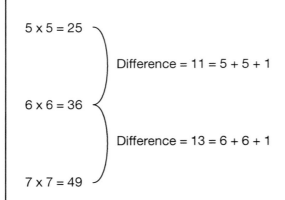

5 x 5 = 25

Difference = 11 = 5 + 5 + 1

6 x 6 = 36

Difference = 13 = 6 + 6 + 1

7 x 7 = 49

What do you think the difference between 7 x 7 and 8 x 8 will be?

How will you work out which two consecutive, or 'next door', square numbers have a difference of 19?

Or a difference of 25?

Or a difference of 101?

Write a rule for finding two consecutive square numbers if you know their difference.

Another problem

25 is a square number because 25 = 5 x 5.
Work out the answer to 4 x 6.

Find the answers to 6 x 6 and 7 x 5.

What do you expect will be the answer to 7 x 7 and 8 x 6?

Copy and complete this table
 2 x 2 =   3 x 1 =
 3 x 3 =   4 x 2 =
 4 x 4 =

Continue up to 10 x 10. Write a rule to describe what is happening.

Next try
 5 x 5 =   7 x 3 =
 6 x 6 =   8 x 4 =   continue to 10 x 10

Write a rule

Now compare
 5 x 5 with (3 x 3) + (2 x 3) + (2 x 3) + 4
 6 x 6 with (4 x 4) + (2 x 4) + (2 x 4) + 4
 7 x 7 with (5 x 5) + (2 x 5) + (2 x 5) + 4 etc

Continue until you have reached 10 x 10.
Can you describe what is happening this time?

Teacher's Notes

If the difference between two consecutive square numbers is known one way to find the two numbers is to subtract one and halve the answer. One half is the first number and the other half, plus one is the other, e.g. if the difference is 49 one the two numbers is 24 and the other is 25.

Another problem

Children may be able to describe what happens orally but may find it very difficult to write it down. However, it is worth encouraging a written explanation.

n^2 and $(n + 1)(n - 1)$ differ by 1,
or
$n^2 - 1 = (n + 1)(n - 1)$

OR $\square$ x $\square$ is one more than $(\square + 1) + (\square - 1)$

where the same number goes into each box.

Exploring Triangular Numbers 1 & 2

You need

Counters in different colours

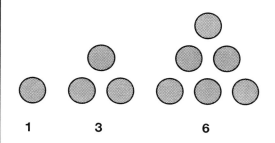

1   3   6

Arrange
  3 counters in a triangle
  6 counters in a triangle
  10 counters in a triangle

Draw diagrams of the triangles.

How many counters will be needed for the next triangle? How many for the next … and the next?

These are called triangular numbers. Draw the diagrams for the first six triangular numbers.

Find the difference between consecutive triangular numbers. (Consecutive numbers are two numbers that are next to each other in a list).

1   3   6   10

2   3   ?

Continue the pattern.

Explain the sequence of numbers.

Can you find a way to work out the tenth triangular number without drawing it?

Can you work out the 20th … or the 100th?

The sequence of triangular numbers is
  1, 3, 6, 10, 15, 21 … …

If these numbers are doubled, we get
  2, 6, 12, 20, 30, 42 … …

We know that 12 = 3 x 4, and that 20 = 4 x 5 …

Write more statements like this. Find some bigger triangular numbers and check if the rule works.

Use this diagram to help explain how the rule works.

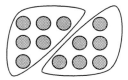

Now add consecutive pairs of triangular numbers, starting with 3 + 6 = 9 and 9 = 3 x 3.

Add the next consecutive pair of triangular numbers, 6 + 10 = 16 and 16 = 4 x 4.

Continue with the pattern.

What do you know about the numbers in your answers?

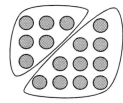

Use these diagrams to explain the patterns.

More Triangles

You need

Triangle MATs of interlocking triangles

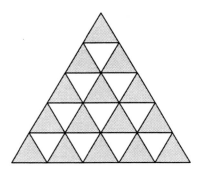

How many small triangles can you see in this diagram altogether?

How many will there be in a diagram with 6 triangles that are the right way up along the base?
Or with 4 … with 3 … with 7?

Of the 25 triangles in this diagram there are 15 the right way up and 10 upside down. 10 + 15 = 25.

Which triangular numbers can you spot in the diagram?

Draw the diagram for the next size of triangle and write number statements about all the small the triangles.

Try some other sizes of triangle and write the number statements.

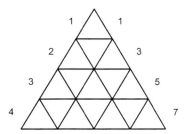

Moving on to Pyramids

Apples can be piled up to make a triangular pyramid (a tetrahedron)

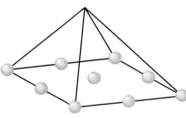

This diagram shows the 4th tetrahedral number.

The first layer contains one apple, the second layer has three, the fourth has six and the fifth has ten apples.

The 2nd tetrahedral number is $1 + 3 = 4$

The 3rd tetrahedral number is $1 + 3 + 6 = 10$.

So the 4th tetrahedral number is $1 + 3 + 6 + 10 = 20$.

Find the 5th tetrahedral number.

Find other tetrahedral numbers and write what you notice about them.

Can you spot these numbers in Pascal's Triangle?

Another way to pile up apples is to make a square-based pyramid.

Only the bottom layer is shown in the diagram. So if there are nine apples in the bottom layer, four in the second and one at the top we get the 3rd pyramid number which is $1 + 4 + 9 = 14$.

Work out the next three pyramid numbers and explain what you did.

What do you notice about the number of apples in each layer?

Imagine a box of chocolates. They are sold in a box shaped like a square-based pyramid, but only the outer layer contains the chocolates. Inside is a cardboard pyramid!

There are four chocolates along the bottom edge of the pyramid.

Work out the number of chocolates in the box.

How many would there be if there were five chocolates along the bottom edge?

What if there were six chocolates?

Explain how you worked out the problem.

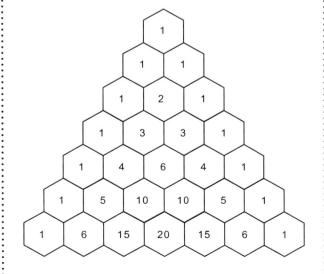

21 Game

You need

A collection of counters, matchsticks or cubes

Version 1

Put 21 counters on the table. Each player, in turn, may remove one or two counters.

The person taking the last one or two counters is the winner.

Play a few games and try to find a winning strategy.

Explain your strategy and then find out if there are any other losing numbers besides one or two.

Version 2

This game is played the same as version 1, except that either one, two or three counters are taken each time.

Investigate which are the losing numbers for this version of the game.

Version 3

In this version of the game each player may take one, three or four counters.

Teacher's Notes

This game, for two players, is similar to *Nim* but that game involves the use of several piles of counters and different rules.

Version 1

To begin with it might help if fewer counters are used, for example 11. Counters are not essential, the game can be played using paper and pencil, but they do make the game more interesting. Coloured matches or cubes could also be used. After a while children should notice that if their opponent leaves them with three counters it is not possible to win.

Ask children to explain why.

Then, ask them to investigate other losing numbers.

Tramlines and Take and Put

Tramlines

You need two red and two green counters (or two 1p coins and two 2p coins) and a game track.

A Game Track

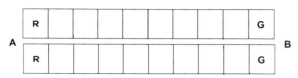

Players take turns to move **ONE** of their counters forward or back any number of spaces along the track. Players may **NOT** jump over one of the opponent's counters or move from one track to another.

The aim of the game is to trap your opponent so they cannot move. For example, in this game if it is Player B's turn she cannot move, so A has won.

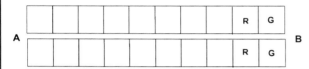

Investigate ways to win the game. Share your ideas with your partner.

Take and Put

You need 20 counters and a Game Board similar to the one below

Place 10 counters on each of the centre circles. At the start of the game the players have no counters in their circles.

In turn, players can **take** counters from one of the centre circles and place them in their circle, or **put** counters from their own circle into a centre circle. If a player can do neither of these two moves that person has lost.

Find out how to win.

Try different numbers of counters and find out how to win with them.

Try to find out why this game is like **Tramlines**.

Teacher's Notes

A useful leading question is to ask, 'What happens if A moves a counter next to one of B's counters?'

e.g. it is B's turn to move

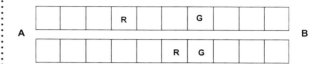

This games is like *Tramlines* because the two centre piles, with 10 counters in each, correspond to the number of squares between the counters on the two tracks; the counters in A's pile correspond to the total number of empty squares behind that player's counters.

Rectangle Game

This game is played on a board which is seven squares by four squares

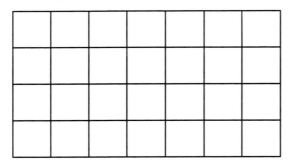

Players take turns to put a O or a X where two lines cross.

The first player to complete a rectangle of any size is the winner.

Do not forget that a square is also a rectangle.

Here is an example

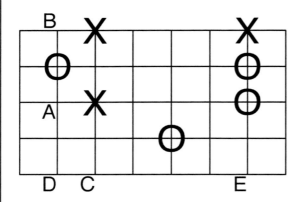

It is the turn of X to move but the player will lose unless the X is placed at A.

Now O must go to B.

If X goes to C, the game can be won by going to D or E.

Teacher's Notes

This activity was first published in *Plus*, Summer 1991. *Plus* is a Mathematical Association publication and ATM would like to thank the MA for their kind permission to use the activity.

Teacher's Notes

Noughts and Crosses

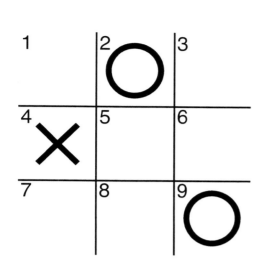

This is a game of noughts and crosses.

You are X. You are thinking of going in square 6.

Is this a good move? Explain your reasons.

What happens if you go in a different square instead of 6? Is this better or worse?

What about trying other squares?

Is there any move which will mean you are certain to win?

Make up another starting position and investigate the same way.

Teacher's Notes

This activity is based on an idea used by Alan Bell in his research on children's concepts of 'proof'. Most children are familiar with the rules of noughts and crosses and so it is a familiar environment for them to explore. Within the setting of a game they are more likely to feel sure their reasoning is correct than in a more abstract mathematical problem-solving setting.

Golden Shapes

Three-piece puzzle   Two-piece puzzle

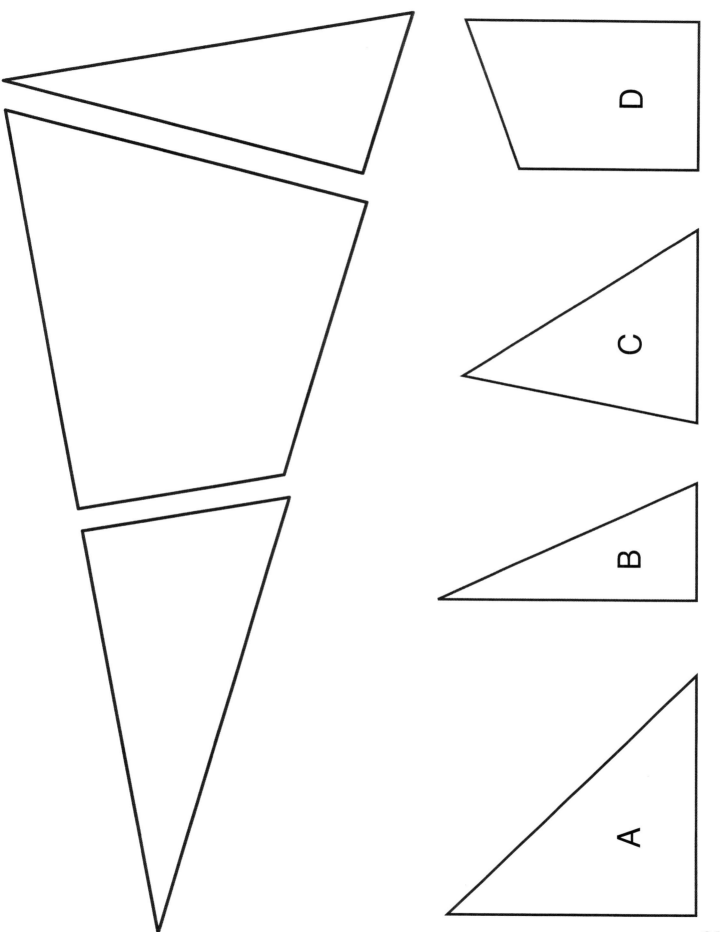

Triangular and Square Arithmogons

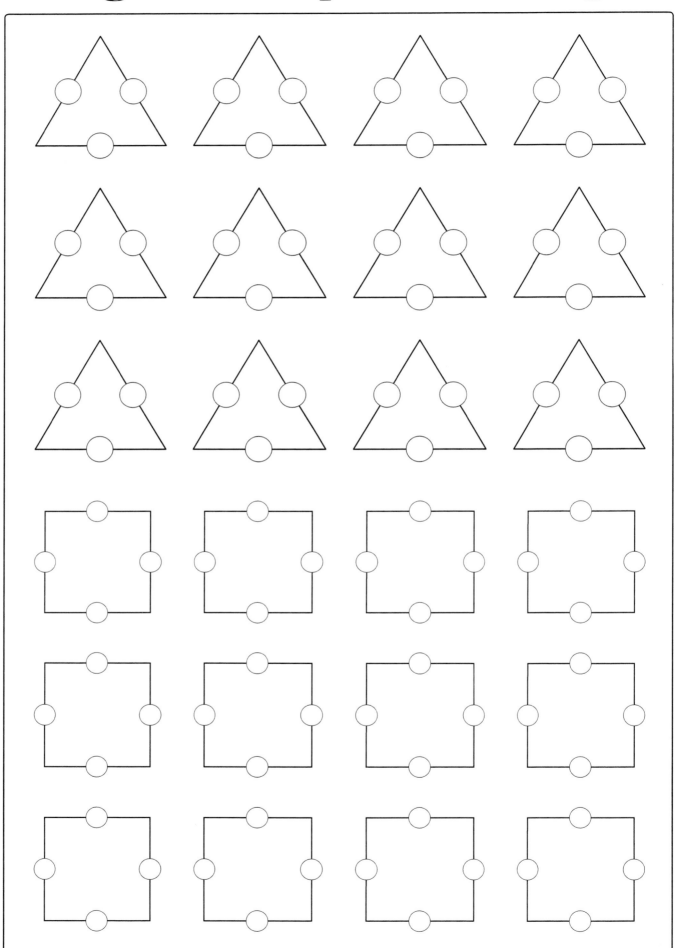

Sort the Symmetry

Maths with Ben - Links to other ATM publications

Page 7

Mathematical Activity Tiles (MATs) are available from the Association of Teachers of Mathematics (ATM) www.atm.org.uk/ The shapes available are equilateral and isosceles triangles, squares, rectangles, and also regular pentagons, hexagons, octagons.

Page 7

Note: A trickier combination problem (which uses Cuisenaire rods) can be found on page 2 of "Everyone is Special" by Mike Ollerton

Pages 9–10

More arithmogon problems can be found on page 27 of "Learning and Teaching Mathematics without a Textbook" by Mike Ollerton

Page 13

Some more problems relating to finding triangles on 'dotty' paper can be found on page 1 of "Forty Problems for the Classroom" by Derek Ball and Nick Eyres

Page 15

A 'similar but different' investigation involving 'flipping triangles' appears on page 15 of "Everyone is Special" by Mike Ollerton

Page 18

You can learn more about "Sorting by Symmetry" in Bob Burn's book of that title.

Page 20

There are many useful web sites explaining the symmetries of wallpaper patterns

For example:
<http://mathworld.wolfram.com/WallpaperGroups.html>
 and
<http://en.wikipedia.org/wiki/Wallpaper_group#Lattice_types>

Page 23

A useful book for exploring number patterns using Multilink is "Linking Cubes and the Learning of Mathematics" by Paul Andrews. See, for example pages 11-15

Page 27

A hard extension to this problem can be found on page 81 of "Linking Cubes and the Learning of Mathematics" by Paul Andrews. However, the pieces could also be used simply as a spatial puzzle.

Page 27

A square pyramid version of the tetrahedral problem using linking cubes is on page 79 of "Linking Cubes and the Learning of Mathematics" by Paul Andrews.

Page 29

A similar game, (Fighting Lizards on page 26) and many other activities, can be found in "People Maths - Hidden Depths" by Alan Bloomfield and Bob Vertes